Peanuts at School

Peanuts at School

Charles M. Schulz

RAVETTE BOOKS

Ravette Books Limited 1989

Printed and bound for Ravette Books Limited,
3 Glenside Estate, Star Road,
Partridge Green, Horsham,
West Sussex RH13 8RA
by Mateu Cromo Artes Gráfica, s.a.

ISBN: 1 85304 174 2

YES, MA'AM... I'M READY..

THIS IS "SHOW AND TELL" TIME...

FOR ALL YOU LUCKY KIDS OUT THERE IN CLASSROOM-LAND I'VE BROUGHT MY FAMOUS LEAF COLLECTION!

BUT FIRST, A WORD FROM MY SPONSOR..

THESE LEAVES ARE BROUGHT TO YOU THROUGH THE COURTESY OF OUR COUNTRY'S TREES

MY LEAF COLLECTION WAS GATHERED FROM MANY LAWNS AND ALONGSIDE MANY CURBS... THESE ARE LEAVES FROM ALL WALKS OF LIFE...

AND NOW A BRIEF WORD FROM MY CO-SPONSOR, THE RAIN...

THE RAIN COMES DOWN FROM THE CLOUDS WHICH ARE IN THE SKY, AND WATERS THE SOIL UPON WHICH SIT THE TREES WHEREON GREW THESE LEAVES...

WHICH BRINGS US BACK TO MY FAMOUS COLLECTION.. YES, MA'AM?

FIRST THEY WANT YOU TO SHOW AND TELL, AND THEN THEY DON'T WANT YOU TO SHOW AND TELL...

SCHULZ

I KNOW THE
ANSWER !
I KNOW THE
ANSWER !

THE ANSWER
IS TWELVE !

IT
ISN'T ?

SIXTEEN ?
NINE ?
FORTY-TWO?
ONE ?

HOW WOULD
IT BE IF I
JUST SPELLED
MISSISSIPPI ?

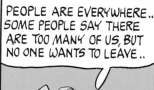

SEVEN O'CLOCK, SALLY... TIME TO GET UP!

GOOD GRIEF... I'VE GOT TO HURRY...

The Incas

The Incas were people who lived a long time ago in Incaland.

They had a highly developed civilization.

They would still be here today, but they lacked motel facilities.

SOME OF MY BEST TERM PAPERS HAVE BEEN WRITTEN BEFORE BREAKFAST!

Bleah!

A "C"?

A "C"? I GOT A "C" ON MY COAT-HANGER SCULPTURE?

HOW COULD ANYONE GET A "C" IN COAT-HANGER SCULPTURE?

MAY I ASK A QUESTION?

WAS I JUDGED ON THE PIECE OF SCULPTURE ITSELF? IF SO, IS IT NOT TRUE THAT TIME ALONE CAN JUDGE A WORK OF ART?

OR WAS I JUDGED ON MY TALENT? IF SO, IS IT RIGHT THAT I BE JUDGED ON A PART OF LIFE OVER WHICH I HAVE NO CONTROL?

IF I WAS JUDGED ON MY EFFORT, THEN I WAS JUDGED UNFAIRLY, FOR I TRIED AS HARD AS I COULD!

WAS I JUDGED ON WHAT I HAD LEARNED ABOUT THIS PROJECT? IF SO, THEN WERE NOT YOU, MY TEACHER, ALSO BEING JUDGED ON YOUR ABILITY TO TRANSMIT YOUR KNOWLEDGE TO ME? ARE YOU WILLING TO SHARE MY "C"?

PERHAPS I WAS BEING JUDGED ON THE QUALITY OF THE COAT HANGER ITSELF OUT OF WHICH MY CREATION WAS MADE...NOW, IS THIS ALSO NOT UNFAIR?

AM I TO BE JUDGED BY THE QUALITY OF COAT HANGERS THAT ARE USED BY THE DRYCLEANING ESTABLISHMENT THAT RETURNS OUR GARMENTS? IS THAT NOT THE RESPONSIBILITY OF MY PARENTS? SHOULD THEY NOT SHARE MY "C"?

"THE SQUEAKY WHEEL GETS THE GREASE!"

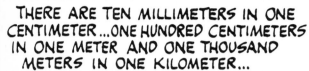

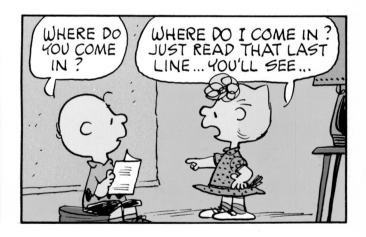

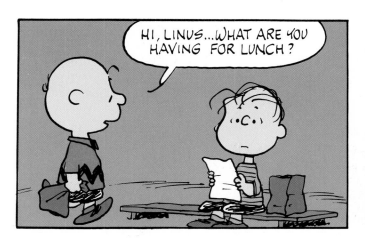

I'M READY!

SO IT'S "SHOW AND TELL" TIME AGAIN, IS IT? WELL, DO I EVER HAVE A SURPRISE FOR YOU TODAY!

I HAVE A LITTLE FILM TO SHOW YOU THAT'S GONNA KNOCK YOUR EYES OUT!

NO, MA'AM... THAT'S ONLY AN EXPRESSION..

ALL RIGHT, IF I CAN HAVE A COUPLE OF YOU STRONG TYPES LIFT THIS PROJECTOR INTO PLACE, WE CAN GET THIS SHOW ON THE ROAD!

NO, LET'S PUT IT ON THAT TABLE BACK THERE... HOW ABOUT YOU FOUR WEIRDOS MOVING THAT TABLE?

AND I'LL NEED A COUPLE MORE TO PUT THIS SCREEN UP... LET'S GO!! ON THE DOUBLE, THERE!

STRETCH THAT CORD ACROSS THE BACK, AND PLUG IT INTO THAT SOCKET IN THE CORNER...

OKAY, SOMEONE RUN DOWN TO THE CUSTODIAN THEN, AND GET AN EXTENSION! YOU THERE, GET GOING!!

NOW, WHAT ABOUT THOSE WINDOW SHADES? LET'S HAVE ALL OF YOU WHO SIT ALONG THE SIDE THERE PULL DOWN THOSE STUPID SHADES..

AND I'LL NEED SOMEONE ON THE LIGHT SWITCH... ONE VOLUNTEER... YOU THERE, HONEY, GET THE SWITCH!

IS THAT THE BELL ALREADY?

OKAY, WE'LL TAKE IT TOMORROW FROM HERE.. EVERYONE BE IN PLACE BY NINE! THANK YOU, AND GOOD MORNING!

YES, MA'AM...THAT'S MY BOOK REPORT..

WHAT ARE THE ODDS ON A LITTLE LOVE AND UNDERSTANDING?

I GOT A "C" IN HISTORY

I GOT A "C" IN MATH...I GOT A "C" IN ENGLISH...AND I GOT A "C" IN READING

I GOT A "C" IN EVERYTHING

I'M A STRAIGHT "BLAH" STUDENT!

WE'RE GOING TO HAVE TO LEARN THE METRIC SYSTEM, FRANKLIN..

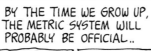

BY THE TIME WE GROW UP, THE METRIC SYSTEM WILL PROBABLY BE OFFICIAL..

ONE INCH IS 2.54 CENTIMETERS.. ONE FOOT IS 0.3048 METERS AND ONE MILE IS 1.609 KILOMETERS...

I'LL NEVER MEASURE ANYTHING AGAIN AS LONG AS I LIVE!

I HAVE A SUGGESTION TO MAKE.

I SUGGEST THAT THE BOARD OF EDUCATION BE TOLD TO BUY A HERD OF TWENTY-FOUR HORSES...

THEN, INSTEAD OF PLAYING A BUNCH OF STUPID GAMES DURING GYM CLASS, WE COULD ALL SADDLE UP, AND GO FOR LONG RIDES...

LOTS OF GOOD SUGGESTIONS NEVER GET OFF THE GROUND!

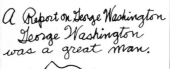

A Report on George Washington George Washington was a great man.

He probably had some faults, but if he did, I don't know what they were.

Which is just as well.

 Theme: Our School

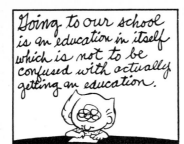 Going to our school is an education in itself which is not to be confused with actually getting an education.

 I DON'T NEED THAT KIND OF TROUBLE!

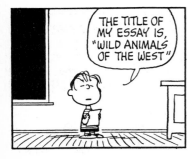 THIS IS AN ARTICLE I'VE WRITTEN FOR SCHOOL CALLED "WILD ANIMALS OF THE WEST"

 "THERE ARE MANY WILD ANIMALS WHO LIVE IN THE WEST..SOME WHO LIVE IN THE MOUNTAINS ARE CALLED MOUNTAIN LIONS..."

 "NOW, OF COURSE, WHERE YOU HAVE MOUNTAINS, YOU HAVE GULLIES... THE WILD ANIMALS WHO LIVE IN THE GULLIES ARE CALLED...."

 "... GULLY CATS"?

 THE TITLE OF MY ESSAY IS, "WILD ANIMALS OF THE WEST"

 OUT WEST THERE ARE MANY GULLIES AND THESE GULLIES ARE FILLED WITH GULLY CATS... GULLY CATS ARE EXTREMELY FIERCE...

 IN FACT, ONE OF THE MOST COMMON OF WESTERN SAYINGS IS THE ONE THAT GOES...

 "NEVER GRIEVE A GULLY CAT!"

 AND THEN I READ MY PAPER ON GULLY CATS TO THE WHOLE CLASS..

 I TOLD ALL ABOUT HOW FIERCE GULLY CATS ARE, AND I EVEN THREW IN A BIT ABOUT HOW THEY ARE IMMUNE TO THE BITE OF THE DREADED QUEEN SNAKE

 WHAT SORT OF A GRADE DID YOUR TEACHER GIVE YOU?

 "NICE TRY"

 THOSE DREAMS I HAVE AT NIGHT ARE GOING TO DRIVE ME CRAZY

 LAST NIGHT I DREAMED THAT LITTLE RED-HAIRED GIRL AND I WERE EATING LUNCH TOGETHER...

 BUT SHE'S GONE..SHE'S MOVED AWAY, AND I DON'T KNOW WHERE SHE LIVES, AND SHE DOESN'T KNOW I EVEN EXIST, AND I'LL NEVER SEE HER AGAIN ...AND...

 I WISH MEN CRIED..

DUCK, BIG BROTHER! HERE COMES ANOTHER DAY!!

WE ALL NEED HOPE, FRANKLIN, DID YOU KNOW THAT?

AND WE ALL NEED MEMORIES... WITHOUT GOOD MEMORIES, LIFE CAN BE PRETTY SKUNGIE...

I HAD THREE GOOD MEMORIES ONCE...

BUT I FORGOT WHAT THEY WERE!

I'M STILL HUNGRY..

I ATE A PEANUT BUTTER SANDWICH, AN APPLE AND TWO COOKIES, BUT I'M STILL HUNGRY..

THAT ALWAYS USED TO BE ENOUGH FOR ME..

I THINK I'VE OUTGROWN MY LUNCH!

TRASH

This report is on sheepherders.

Sheepherders raise lambs from which we get lambchops.

They also raise sheep from which we get sheepchops.

SHEEPCHOPS?

HOW ABOUT A GAME OF MARBLES AFTER SCHOOL, FRANKLIN?

I CAN'T..I HAVE A GUITAR LESSON AT THREE-THIRTY...

RIGHT AFTER THAT I HAVE LITTLE LEAGUE, AND THEN SWIM CLUB, AND THEN DINNER AND THEN A '4H' MEETING

I LEAD A VERY ACTIVE TUESDAY!

Ten milligrams equals one centigram.

Ten decigrams equals one gram.

Ten grams equals one grampa.

KEEP GOING... I CAN HARDLY WAIT TO SEE WHAT COMES NEXT...

I'M DOOMED!

I HAVE TO WRITE A REPORT ON RIVERS AND IT'S DUE NEXT WEEK, AND I JUST KNOW I'LL GET A FAILING GRADE!

WHY DON'T YOU WORK REAL HARD AND TURN IN THE BEST REPORT THAT YOU CAN POSSIBLY WRITE?

THAT NEVER OCCURRED TO ME!

This is the last English theme of the year, and it is a good thing.

What a waste these themes are. What a drag. What a bummer.

THAT'S PROBABLY NOT A GOOD IDEA...

This is my theme on Memorial Day which I am writing on Monday because there is no school today.

Everyone is observing Memorial Day today so they can have a three-day weekend and go water skiing.

Which hasn't much to do with Memorial Day which is really tomorrow.

THIS IS THE SORT THEME WHERE YOU GET EITHER AN "A" OR AN "F"!

TRUE! FALSE! TRUE!

TRUE! FALSE! FALSE! TRUE! FALSE! FALSE! TRUE! FALSE!

TRUE! FALSE! TRUE! TRUE! FALSE! TRUE! TRUE! TRUE! TRUE! FALSE! TRUE! FALSE!

AND ONE GOOD OLD FASHIONED **MAYBE**!!

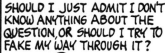
AN ESSAY QUESTION! GOOD GRIEF! I'M DOOMED!!

SHOULD I JUST ADMIT I DON'T KNOW ANYTHING ABOUT THE QUESTION, OR SHOULD I TRY TO FAKE MY WAY THROUGH IT?

IF I ADMIT I DON'T KNOW ANYTHING, I FAIL FOR SURE! BANG! THAT'S IT! NO WAY! HOWEVER, IF I FAKE IT, I'VE GOT AT LEAST A MILLION-TO-ONE CHANCE...

SO HERE I GO!!

THIS TEST IS TOO HARD...

YOU KNOW WHAT WE NEED, MA'AM?

WHAT WE NEED IS A GOOD OLD-FASHIONED OPEN-BOOK TEST... I'M GOOD AT THOSE...

YOU TELL ME WHAT BOOK TO OPEN, AND I'LL OPEN IT!!!

WE GOT OUR TESTS BACK...

I WONDER WHAT GRADE I GOT... I HATE TO LOOK...

"Z MINUS"?!!

PRINCIPAL'S OFFICE

YES, SIR... I'D LIKE TO PROTEST A GRADE THAT MY TEACHER GAVE ME ON OUR LAST TEST...

LOOK... A "Z MINUS"!

THAT'S NOT A GRADE... THAT'S SARCASM!!

HOW ABOUT THAT, FRANKLIN? DON'T TELL ME THE SQUEAKY WHEEL DOESN'T GET THE GREASE!

I WENT TO THE PRINCIPAL AND PROTESTED THAT "Z MINUS" THE TEACHER GAVE ME ON OUR TEST...

THEY MUST HAVE HAD A LITTLE TALK BECAUSE SHE CHANGED MY GRADE

SHE RAISED IT TO A "Z"!!

This is my report on rain. Rain is water which does not come out of faucets.

If it were not for rain, we would not get wet walking to school and get a sore throat and stay home which is not a bad idea.

Rain was the inspiration for that immortal poem, "Rain, rain, go away. Come again some other day."

After a storm, the rain goes down the drain which is where I sometimes feel my education is also going. End of report

HA, THERE YOU ARE, YOU STUPID SCHOOL!

YOU CAN'T GET ME NOW BECAUSE THIS IS SUMMER VACATION! I'M FREE! DO YOU HEAR ME? FREE!

IT MAKES YOU MAD, DOESN'T IT? BUT YOU CAN'T GET ME NOW!! I'M FREE!!!

YOUR SISTER TALKS TO SCHOOL BUILDINGS

TAKE THAT, YOU STUPID SCHOOL!!

BOOT!

I LIKE SUMMER VACATION... IT'S THE ONLY TIME WHEN YOU CAN RUN RIGHT UP TO A SCHOOL AND KICK IT!

I THINK I'LL DO MY SUMMER SCHOOL THEME ON JOHNNY SEBASTIAN BACH...

NOT "JOHNNY"... "JOHANN"!

THAT'S WHAT I SAID..."JOHANNY"

NOT "JOHANNY"! JOHANN!! JOHANN SEBASTIAN BACH!

WHAT ABOUT HIM?

MAYBE I'LL WRITE ABOUT BOBBY ORR...

SUMMER IS ALMOST OVER!

SCHOOL STARTS IN THREE WEEKS!!

PANIC IN THE STREETS!

PANIC IN THE STREETS?

STUDYING POETRY SPOILS THE POEMS

WHY DO WE HAVE TO TRY TO EXPLAIN A POEM?

THAT'S LIKE TRYING TO EXPLAIN A SUMMER SKY, OR A WINTER MOON...

..OR A PRETTY FACE!

I LEARNED TWO THINGS IN SCHOOL TODAY

I LEARNED THAT IF YOU DON'T WATCH WHERE YOU'RE GOING, YOU CAN GET KNOCKED DOWN IN THE HALL...

AND I ALSO LEARNED THAT THE DRINKING FOUNTAIN IS OUT OF ORDER!

IT'S NOT OFTEN THAT YOU CAN LEARN TWO NEW THINGS IN ONE DAY!

Report; Agriculture

This report is on melons. Melons have to be planted between May 15th and June 5th.

I don't know what you do if you happen to be out of town.

I'm glad I'm not a melon farmer.

WHO WAS THE FATHER OF HENRY IV?

I COULD NOT POSSIBLY CARE LESS!

I'M SORRY... I APOLOGIZE..

THAT WAS JUST A GUT REACTION

WHAT ARE YOU READING, FRANKLIN?

IT'S A BOOK ON PSYCHOLOGY.. FROM WHAT I UNDERSTAND, IT SEEMS TO BE PRETTY GOOD..

FORGET IT, FRANKLIN...

NO BOOK ON PSYCHOLOGY CAN BE ANY GOOD IF ONE CAN UNDERSTAND IT!

FIRST YOU SWOOP IN ALL THE I'S....THEN YOU POP IN ALL THE DOTS....

IF THEY COME OUT EVEN, THAT'S GOOD PENMANSHIP!

ARE THOSE M'S OR N'S?

NEITHER

THOSE ARE MMMMMMM'S!

LOOK AT THAT... A PERFECT G!

DO YOU WANT IT? DO YOU WANT TO FRAME IT, AND HANG IT IN YOUR ROOM?
NO, THANK YOU

WHAT'S THE MATTER, DON'T YOU APPRECIATE GOOD PENMANSHIP?!

WHAT ARE THOSE?

THOSE ARE U'S AND W'S!
YOU SHOULDN'T RUN THEM ALL TOGETHER LIKE THAT

IF IT DOESN'T BOTHER THEM, WHY SHOULD IT BOTHER YOU?

THOSE ARE NICE LOOKING T'S

THOSE AREN'T T'S...THOSE ARE TELEPHONE POLES...I'M DRAWING A PICTURE DEPICTING THE CHANGE OF THE WEST

I'M GOING TO SHOW HOW THE TELEPHONE POLES LED THE GREAT MOVEMENT OF PEOPLE ACROSS THE LAND!

I WAS JUST KIDDING YOU...THEY'RE REALLY T'S!

 EDUCATION IS IMPORTANT, FRANKLIN

 SAY, FOR INSTANCE, THAT I'M THE MANAGER OF A MAJOR-LEAGUE BALL CLUB AND I'M TAKING THE LINEUP OUT TO THE UMPIRE...

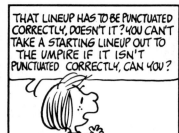 THAT LINEUP HAS TO BE PUNCTUATED CORRECTLY, DOESN'T IT? YOU CAN'T TAKE A STARTING LINEUP OUT TO THE UMPIRE IF IT ISN'T PUNCTUATED CORRECTLY, CAN YOU?

 EDUCATION IS IMPORTANT, FRANKLIN!

 ABRAHAM LINCOLN USED TO DO HIS HOMEWORK ON THE BACK OF A COAL SHOVEL

 ONE DAY, HIS DAD SAID TO HIM, "SORRY, SON, I HAVE TO USE THE SHOVEL," AND WIPED OUT POOR ABE'S ENGLISH REPORT!

 WELL, IT COULD HAVE HAPPENED!!

 I'M TRYING, MARCIE, BUT I'M STILL DOING LOUSY IN SCHOOL

 MAYBE YOU NEED TO EAT A BETTER BREAKFAST, SIR, OR HAVE YOUR EYES CHECKED OR START GOING TO BED EARLIER

YOU'VE NEVER UNDERSTOOD, HAVE YOU, MARCIE, THAT WHEN A PERSON COMPLAINS, HE DOESN'T WANT A SOLUTION, HE WANTS SYMPATHY!!

 NO, I ADMIT I'VE NEVER UNDERSTOOD THAT, SIR... STOP CALLING ME "SIR"!

 YOU NEVER HAD ANY EDUCATION, SNOOPY...

 AND YET YOU SEEM TO KNOW A LOT...

 YOU NEVER WENT TO COLLEGE OR ANYTHING..

 THAT'S NOT QUITE TRUE... ACTUALLY, I DID GREAT IN NURSERY SCHOOL!

 MY STORY TAKES PLACE IN THE NAPA VALLEY IN CALIFORNIA...

 THIS IS WINE COUNTRY, AND ON ONE OF THE RANCHES, THERE LIVED A RHINOCEROS WHO BECAME SO FOND OF DRINKING WINE, THEY CALLED HIM THE "WINO RHINO"!

HAHAHAHA

RATS!

STUPID SCHOOL!

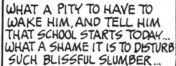

YOU'RE JUST WAITING FOR TOMORROW, AREN'T YOU, SO YOU CAN TORTURE A BUNCH OF INNOCENT KIDS?!

WELL, YOU WON'T GET AWAY WITH IT FOREVER!

SOMEBODY GET THIS KID AWAY FROM ME!

HE LOOKS SO PEACEFUL LYING THERE...

WHAT A PITY TO HAVE TO WAKE HIM, AND TELL HIM THAT SCHOOL STARTS TODAY... WHAT A SHAME IT IS TO DISTURB SUCH BLISSFUL SLUMBER...

PSST, LINUS...

SCHOOL STARTS TODAY !!!

THE ANSWER IS NINE!

IT ISN'T? RATS!

THE FIRST MINUTE OF THE FIRST DAY OF SCHOOL, AND I GET THE FIRST WRONG ANSWER

DO I GET ANYTHING FOR SETTING A RECORD?

YOU CALL YOURSELF A SCHOOL BUILDING!

JUST THINK OF ALL THE MISERY YOU'VE CAUSED!

DOESN'T YOUR CONSCIENCE BOTHER YOU?

IT'S A LIVING!

JUST BECAUSE YOU'RE A SCHOOL, DON'T THINK YOU'RE BEYOND CRITICISM!

ON THE CONTRARY!

I SAY THAT IT'S TIME WE ALL TAKE A CLOSER LOOK AT SOME OF OUR CHERISHED INSTITUTIONS!

LOOK CLOSER, KID, AND I'LL DROP A BRICK ON YOU!!

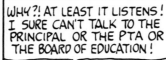

THE REASON I'M HERE IS I HAVE A MESSAGE FOR YOU..

MY LITTLE SISTER WASN'T FEELING WELL SO SHE DIDN'T GO TO SCHOOL TODAY...AS YOU KNOW...YOU BEING THE SCHOOL

ANYWAY, THAT'S THE MESSAGE.. I HOPE I HAVEN'T BOTHERED YOU OR ANYTHING... I'LL PROBABLY SEE YOU TOMORROW...

I'LL BE HERE

DID I JUST SEE YOU TALKING TO THAT SCHOOL BUILDING?

I DID, DIDN'T I? YOU'VE FINALLY CRACKED UP, HAVEN'T YOU, CHARLIE BROWN?

YOU HAVE TO BE CRAZY, YOU KNOW, TO STAND AND TALK TO A STUPID BRICK BUILDING!

BONK!!

THE PRINCIPAL'S OFFICE? ME?! YES, MA'AM..

I HATE GOING TO THE PRINCIPAL'S OFFICE! I ALWAYS HAVE THE FEELING THAT I'LL NEVER COME BACK, OR THAT NO ONE WILL EVER SEE ME AGAIN...

GOOD MORNING... I WAS TOLD TO REPORT TO THE PRINCIPAL...

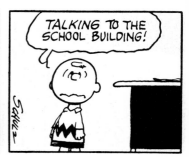

AM I ALLOWED ONE PHONE CALL?

ME?

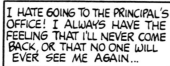

ME? WRITING ON THE SCHOOL BUILDING?!! NO, SIR, I DIDN'T WRITE ON THE SCHOOL BUILDING! NO, SIR, ABSOLUTELY NOT!

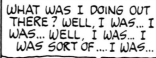

WHAT WAS I DOING OUT THERE? WELL, I WAS... I WAS... WELL, I WAS... I WAS SORT OF.... I WAS...

TALKING TO THE SCHOOL BUILDING!

BOY, DID YOU EVER GET ME IN TROUBLE!

SOMEONE SAW ME TALKING TO THE SCHOOL BUILDING, AND REPORTED ME TO THE PRINCIPAL! HE THINKS I'M CRAZY...HE WANTS ME TO SEE OUR FAMILY DOCTOR...

I HOPE YOU REALIZE I'VE BEEN COVERING UP FOR YOU! I HOPE YOU REALIZE I'VE BEEN SUFFERING IN SILENCE!

I'VE BEEN SUFFERING IN SILENCE FOR SIXTY YEARS, KID!

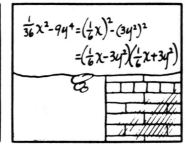

THIS IS A SCHOOL PROJECT.. I'M DRAWING A MAP OF THE WHOLE WORLD...

I HAVE TO PUT IN ALL THE COUNTRIES, AND ALL THE CAPITALS, AND ALL THE MOUNTAINS, AND THE RIVERS, AND THE TREES, AND THE ROCKS AND ALL THE PEOPLE!

DOT DOT DOT DOT DOT DOT DOT DOT DOT DOT DOT

THIS IS THE HARDEST PART.. DRAWING IN ALL THEIR EYES...

I'M ALSO PUTTING IN ALL THE DOGS AND CATS AND BUGS..DO YOU REALIZE HOW MANY BUGS THERE ARE IN THE WORLD?

THERE! IT'S FINISHED! NOW, I CAN GO TO BED KNOWING IT'S BEEN A JOB WELL DONE...

SHE SURE GETS INVOLVED IN SOME WEIRD PROJECTS

DOT DOT DOT DOT DOT DOT DOT DOT

I THOUGHT YOU WERE IN BED...I THOUGHT YOU WERE FINISHED...

I FORGOT HORSES AND COWS...

QUESTION NUMBER ONE...
WHAT IS THE CAPITAL OF
CAMEROUN?

Answer: When I grow up, I am going to be a hair dresser, and hair dressers obviously don't have to know such things.

QUESTION NUMBER TWO...
WHAT IS THE LENGTH OF
THE RIO GRANDE RIVER?

Answer: When I grow up, I will also probably be a housewife, and could not care less about the length of the Rio Grande river.

QUESTION NUMBER THREE... WHAT IS THE
NAME OF THE LARGEST PYRAMID?

Answer: When I grow up, I will undoubtedly be a member of the smart set.

We members of the smart set rarely discuss such things as pyramids.

THIS IS AN
EASY TEST..

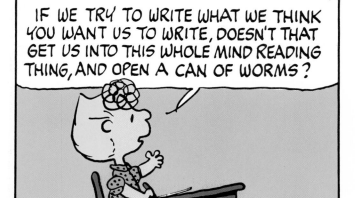

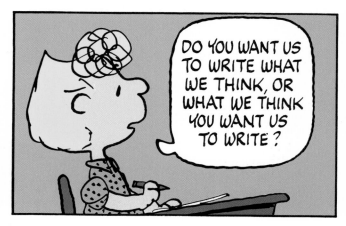

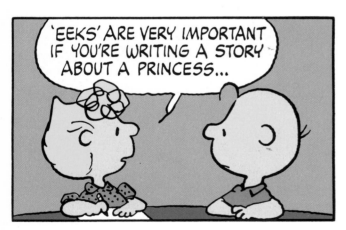

THAT SHOULD BE "DEAR"

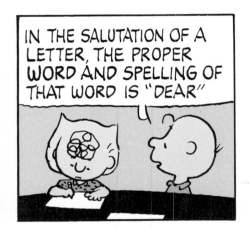

IN THE SALUTATION OF A LETTER, THE PROPER WORD AND SPELLING OF THAT WORD IS "DEAR"

Deer are beautiful animals found in most parts of the world.

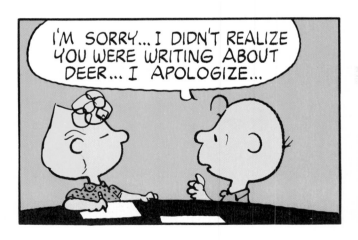

I'M SORRY... I DIDN'T REALIZE YOU WERE WRITING ABOUT DEER... I APOLOGIZE...

WELL, I SHOULD HOPE SO! IT SEEMS TO ME THAT A LOT OF THE PROBLEMS IN THIS WORLD ARE CAUSED BY PEOPLE WHO CRITICIZE OTHER PEOPLE BEFORE THEY KNOW WHAT THEY'RE TALKING ABOUT!

Dear Grandma,

WHAT KIND OF A REPORT CARD DO YOU CALL THIS?

I DIDN'T EVEN GET ANY GRADES...

ALL IT SAYS IS, "GOOD HUSTLE!"

FOR "SHOW AND TELL" TODAY I HAVE BROUGHT YOU A LOCAL HERO!

THIS LITTLE FELLOW HERE BROKE HIS FIFTH METATARSAL WHILE RESCUING THREE AIRLINE STEWARDESSES ON RUNAWAY HORSES!

LISTEN CAREFULLY, FOR THIS IS THE WAY IT ALL HAPPENED...

INCIDENTALLY, MA'AM, ARE WE GRADED ON TRUTH AND ACCURACY?

FOR "SHOW AND TELL" I BRING YOU THE TALE OF A HERO...

YOU REALIZE, OF COURSE, I'M NOT BRINGING HIS TAIL... HE BROUGHT HIS OWN TAIL... WHAT I'M BRINGING IS HIS TALE! YOU KNOW WHAT I MEAN?

BOOT!

OKAY.... ON WITH THE STORY...

TO BEGIN OUR STORY WE MUST GO BACK SEVERAL YEARS...

WE MUST GO BACK TO THE CHILDHOOD YEARS OF OUR THREE AIRLINE STEWARDESSES, EVELYN, PAT AND SHIRLEY...

EVELYN WAS BORN IN MISSOURI, PAT IN WISCONSIN AND SHIRLEY IN PENNSYLVANIA... NOW, WHEN EVELYN WAS ONLY THIRTEEN, SHE...

I'M SORRY, MA'AM... YES, I UNDERSTAND... WELL, JUST HOW MUCH TIME DO WE HAVE?

..AN' THAT'S THE END OF OUR HERO'S STORY!

TO TELL YOU THE TRUTH, HE WASN'T A HERO AT ALL.. ACTUALLY, HE BROKE HIS STUPID FOOT WHEN HE TRIPPED OVER HIS OWN SUPPER DISH!

THIS CONCLUDES OUR PORTION OF "SHOW AND TELL"

WE NOW SWITCH YOU BACK TO YOUR LOCAL STATIONS!

WOULD YOU REPEAT THE QUESTION, MA'AM?

COULD YOU REPHRASE THE QUESTION, MA'AM?

MAYBE YOU COULD ASK ME A DIFFERENT QUESTION...

HOW WOULD IT BE IF I WENT OUT THE DOOR, AND CAME BACK IN AGAIN?

MY HISTORY REPORT IS ON WASHINGTON, D.C.

D.C. STANDS FOR DOCTOR... DOCTOR WASHINGTON WAS AN OPHTHALMOLOGIST... HIS BEST FRIEND WAS NAMED BUNKER HILL

ONE DAY ON THE BATTLEFIELD, DOCTOR WASHINGTON LOOKED AT BUNKER HILL, AND SAID, "THERE'S SOMETHING WRONG WITH THE WHITES OF YOUR EYES!"

AS A REWARD FOR SAVING HIS FRIEND'S VISION, THE PEOPLE VOTED TO MAKE DOCTOR WASHINGTON THEIR COACH!

MA'AM?

I'M NOT SURE ABOUT THIS FIRST QUESTION...

AS A MATTER OF FACT, I DON'T THINK I CAN ANSWER ANY OF THESE QUESTIONS

MAYBE I COULD JUST HELP THE CUSTODIAN SWEEP THE HALLS...

I'M HAVING TROUBLE IN SCHOOL, MARCIE..

MY DAD IS OUT OF TOWN AGAIN, BUT I TALKED WITH HIM ON THE PHONE..HE SAID I COULD TRANSFER TO A PRIVATE SCHOOL IF I WANTED TO...

YOU DON'T THINK THE GOVERNMENT WOULD BE OFFENDED IF I LEFT THE PUBLIC SCHOOL, DO YOU?

I WOULDN'T WANT ANYONE TO THINK I'M A SNOB..

THE GOVERNMENT WOULD UNDERSTAND, SIR!

A PRIVATE SCHOOL MIGHT DO ME A LOT OF GOOD CHUCK

I MIGHT EVEN BECOME ONE OF THE BEAUTIFUL PEOPLE! WOULDN'T THAT BE SOMETHING?

I CAN SEE YOU NOW IN A WHITE BLOUSE AND A BLUE SKIRT RUNNING OUT TO PLAY FIELD HOCKEY...

DON'T HASSLE ME WITH YOUR SARCASM, CHUCK!

THESE ARE BROCHURES FOR PRIVATE SCHOOLS MARCIE...

HERE'S ONE THAT ADVERTISES "ADVENTURE, FELLOWSHIP AND CREATIVITY". AND HERE'S ONE THAT HAS AN INDOOR RIDING RING AND AN OLYMPIC POOL!

HERE'S ONE THAT HAS FIELD TRIPS TO NORWAY AND HOLLAND!

HERE'S ONE SIR, THAT EMPHASIZES REMEDIAL READING...

ARE YOU TRYING TO BRING ME BACK DOWN TO EARTH, MARCIE?

SNOOPY, I HAVE A PROBLEM...

MY DAD IS WILLING TO SEND ME TO A PRIVATE SCHOOL, BUT THEY ALL COST FOUR OR FIVE THOUSAND DOLLARS

I CAN'T ASK HIM TO SPEND THAT MUCH MONEY ON ME... WHAT SHOULD I DO?

"ACE OBEDIENCE SCHOOL... COMPLETE TRAINING... TWENTY-FIVE DOLLARS"

I THINK I'VE FOUND A PRIVATE SCHOOL, CHUCK...

SNOOPY GAVE ME THIS BROCHURE...THEY ONLY CHARGE TWENTY-FIVE DOLLARS...

"ACE OBEDIENCE SCHOOL"?!

IT LOOKS LIKE KIND OF A FUN PLACE...

EVERY STUDENT IN THE SCHOOL SEEMS TO HAVE A PET...

YOU'RE GOING TO ENROLL IN THE "ACE OBEDIENCE SCHOOL"?

BUT THAT ISN'T A...

DON'T TRY TO TALK ME OUT OF IT, CHUCK...

I NEED A GOOD EDUCATION... EVEN IF I BECOME A GREAT ATHLETE, I KNOW I'LL STILL NEED A GOOD EDUCATION

THANKS AGAIN, SNOOPY, FOR GIVING ME THE SCHOOL BROCHURE

I THINK MAYBE I'D BETTER LEAVE TOWN...

IS THIS THE "ACE OBEDIENCE SCHOOL"?

IT IS? GOOD! I'M HERE TO ENROLL! DOG? NO, MA'AM, I DIDN'T BRING A DOG...

I NOTICE THAT A LOT OF YOUR STUDENTS DO HAVE DOGS, DON'T THEY?

IS THIS ONE OF THOSE PROGRESSIVE SCHOOLS?

 WISH ME LUCK, MARCIE...I'M OFF TO PRIVATE SCHOOL!

 I'M GOING TO THE "ACE OBEDIENCE SCHOOL"! IT'S KIND OF A STRANGE NAME, BUT IT PROBABLY MEANS THAT THEY STRESS DISCIPLINE...

 THAT'S OKAY WITH ME... I'M THE FIRST ONE TO ADMIT THAT MY STUDY HABITS AREN'T TOO GOOD

 I WONDER, THOUGH, WHY WE'RE SUPPOSED TO TAKE ALONG A CHOKE-CHAIN

 ARF ARF ARF ARF — YES, SIR, I'M ONE OF YOUR NEW STUDENTS..

 ARF ARF ARF ARF — DO I GET A DESK, SIR?

 ARF ARF — I SEE...YES, I NOTICE YOU DON'T HAVE ANY DESKS...

 ARF ARF ARF — EXCUSE ME, BUT ARE THE CLASSROOMS ALWAYS THIS NOISY?

 HOW WAS YOUR FIRST DAY AT PRIVATE SCHOOL, SIR?

 WAS THE "ACE OBEDIENCE SCHOOL" ALL YOU EXPECTED?

 MORE, MARCIE, A LOT MORE! THEY REALLY STRESS MANNERS AND SOCIAL GRACES...

 WE SPENT THE WHOLE FIRST DAY JUST LEARNING HOW TO SIT!

 THE "ACE OBEDIENCE SCHOOL" HAS CHANGED MY WHOLE LIFE, CHUCK!

 REMEMBER HOW DISCOURAGED I USED TO GET ABOUT SCHOOL?

 AT THE "ACE OBEDIENCE SCHOOL" THEY DON'T LET YOU GET DISCOURAGED...

 EVERY TIME YOU DO SOMETHING RIGHT THEY PAT YOU ON THE HEAD!

 I THINK YOU'RE IN TROUBLE..

 PEPPERMINT PATTY THINKS SHE'S IN A PRIVATE SCHOOL... WHAT'S GOING TO HAPPEN WHEN SHE FINDS OUT SHE'S IN DOG TRAINING CLASSES?

 SHE'S GOING TO COME AROUND HERE LOOKING FOR A CERTAIN BEAGLE WHO GAVE HER A BROCHURE ON THE "ACE OBEDIENCE SCHOOL"

 BEAGLE? WHAT BEAGLE?

FETCH? YES, SIR!

"FETCH" MEANS TO RETRIEVE OR TO GO GET SOMETHING...

OH, I'M SORRY, SIR... I THOUGHT YOU WANTED THE DEFINITION...

THIS MUST BE THE "LEARN BY DOING" METHOD...

DOING YOUR HOMEWORK, EH, MARCIE?

AT THE "ACE OBEDIENCE SCHOOL" WE DON'T HAVE HOMEWORK...

OF COURSE, WE PRIVATE SCHOOL STUDENTS DESERVE A FEW PRIVILEGES, I GUESS... AFTER ALL, WE DO PAY EXTRA MONEY, AND WE ARE SPECIAL AND WE...

HEEL, SIR!!

WHAT?

I DON'T UNDERSTAND THE OTHER PUPILS IN THIS SCHOOL...

I'M THE ONLY ONE WHO EVER GETS OUT HERE, AND JUMPS THESE HURDLES...

THEY WATCH THEIR DOGS JUMP WHILE THEY JUST STAND AROUND...

I'M SURPRISED THE SCHOOL ALLOWS LAZY STUDENTS LIKE THAT TO HAVE PETS...

MY DIPLOMA? YOU MEAN I'VE GRADUATED ALREADY?

I CAN'T BELIEVE IT! I'VE GRADUATED FROM THE "ACE OBEDIENCE SCHOOL"!

HEY, MARCIE! I DON'T HAVE TO GO TO SCHOOL ANY MORE! I'VE GRADUATED!

YOU MUST BE VERY PROUD, SIR...

IT'S AN EFFORT TO REMAIN HUMBLE, MARCIE!

THAT'S RIGHT, CHUCK... I GRADUATED!

NO, I DON'T EVER HAVE TO GO TO SCHOOL AGAIN... I'M A CERTIFIED GRADUATE OF THE "ACE OBEDIENCE SCHOOL..."

THANKS, CHUCK...WELL, YOU KNOW HOW MUCH I'VE ALWAYS WANTED A GOOD EDUCATION... AND YOU KNOW WHAT I'VE ALWAYS SAID...

A GOOD EDUCATION IS THE NEXT BEST THING TO A PUSHY MOTHER!

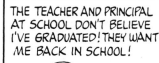

MA'AM, DID I UNDERSTAND CORRECTLY?

YOU WANT US TO READ A BOOK DURING CHRISTMAS VACATION? A REAL BOOK? A WHOLE BOOK?!!

YOU'RE JUST KIDDING, AREN'T YOU MA'AM? SURE, YOU ARE! YOU'RE NOT? YOU MUST BE! YOU'RE NOT?

HAPPY HOLIDAYS!

GUESS WHAT, CHUCK! DISASTER TIME!

OUR TEACHER WANTS US TO READ A BOOK DURING CHRISTMAS VACATION... GOT ANY SUGGESTIONS?

ON WHAT BOOK TO READ?

NO, ON HOW TO GET OUT OF IT!

I'M NOT GOING TO HAVE TO READ A BOOK, MARCIE

SEE? "A TALE OF TWO CITIES" WAS JUST ON TV! I WATCHED THE MOVIE SO NOW I WON'T HAVE TO READ THE BOOK

THE ONLY THING I DIDN'T UNDERSTAND WERE THE PARTS ABOUT THE SHAMPOO, THE SOAP AND THE COFFEE...

THOSE WERE THE COMMERCIALS, SIR!

I'D LIKE TO READ THIS BOOK, MARCIE, BUT I'M KIND OF AFRAID

I HAD A GRANDFATHER WHO DIDN'T THINK MUCH OF READING...

HE ALWAYS SAID THAT IF YOU READ TOO MANY BOOKS, YOUR HEAD WOULD FALL OFF...

YOU START THE FIRST CHAPTER, SIR, AND I'LL HOLD ONTO YOUR HEAD!

WHY AREN'T YOU READING YOUR BOOK, SIR?

IT'S TOO NICE A DAY TO STAY INSIDE AND READ, MARCIE...BESIDES, I HAVE TO BUILD THIS SNOWMAN...

IF I DON'T DO IT, NO ONE ELSE WILL, AND HE'LL NEVER EXIST...I'M HIS CREATOR! IT'S MY DUTY TO GIVE HIM LIFE!

THIS SNOWMAN HAS A RIGHT TO LIVE, MARCIE!

YOU'RE WEIRD, SIR!

SNOOPY, I HAVE TO READ A BOOK THIS WEEK...

DO YOU HAVE SOMETHING GOOD?

"IT WAS A DARK AND STORMY NIGHT... SUDDENLY, A SHOT RANG OUT!"

I REALLY DON'T CARE MUCH FOR MYSTERIES...

IT'S NOT A MYSTERY, IT'S A GOTHIC!

YOU SHOULDN'T BE OUT HERE SKATING, SIR...

YOU SHOULD BE HOME READING YOUR BOOK

WHAT ARE YOU, MARCIE, MY CONSCIENCE?

IF I WERE YOUR CONSCIENCE, SIR, I'D WHIP YOU INTO SHAPE!

IF YOU WERE MY CONSCIENCE, MARCIE, I'D HAVE YOU TRANSFERRED!

ALL RIGHT MARCIE...WHAT BOOK SHOULD I READ?

HOW ABOUT ONE BY KATHERINE ANNE PORTER, OR JOYCE CAROL OATES OR PAMELA HANSFORD JOHNSON?

FORGET IT MARCIE... ALL THOSE AUTHORS HAVE THREE NAMES...

BY THE TIME I FINISHED READING THE AUTHOR'S NAME, I'D BE TOO TIRED TO READ THE BOOK!

YOU'RE REALLY WEIRD, SIR!

ARE YOU READING YOUR BOOK, SIR?

NO, I'M WATCHING TV, MARCIE...

HOMEWORK IS HOMEWORK, SIR... WE'LL ALWAYS HAVE IT WITH US...

STOP BUGGING ME, MARCIE!

DEATH AND TAXES, SIR!

CHRISTMAS VACATION READING REPORT!

READING IS ONE OF MY FAVORITE PASTIMES...

I CAN'T STAND TO LISTEN TO THIS...

I READ EVERY DAY! AND YOU KNOW WHAT I READ?

A CEREAL BOX!

AUGHH!

THERE'S NOTHING WRONG WITH READING CEREAL BOXES...

SOME OF THE BEST STORIES I'VE EVER READ WERE ON CEREAL BOXES...AND YOU DON'T HAVE TO TURN ANY PAGES!

I PREDICT THAT SOME DAY A CEREAL BOX WILL WIN THE PULITZER PRIZE!

SEE, MARCIE? I DID IT!

YOU'RE WEIRD, SIR...

SHE'S TALKING TO YOU, MARCIE...

MA'AM?

MY BOOK REPORT? OH, GOOD GRIEF!

SHE WAS SO BUSY BUGGING ME, MA'AM, THAT SHE FORGOT TO READ ANYTHING HERSELF!

TURN AROUND, MARCIE... I CAN'T AFFORD TO ASSOCIATE WITH SOMEONE WHO DOESN'T DO HER HOMEWORK!

THIS IS A STORY ABOUT MY UNCLE

MY UNCLE NEVER MISSED A DAY'S WORK IN HIS LIFE UNTIL ONE DAY WHEN HE FELL INTO A ROUTINE!

HAHAHAHA

YES, MA'AM

English Report— "Familiar Quotations"

My favorite "Familiar Quotation" is "Drop Dead!"

It is a very useful quotation. It can be used for almost any occasion.

GOOD GRIEF!

DROP DEAD!!

HEY, MARCIE... WHAT'S THE ANSWER TO THE THIRD QUESTION?

WHY SHOULD I TELL YOU?

3. Why should I tell you?

THANKS, MARCIE...WE'LL PROBABLY BE THE ONLY ONES IN THE WHOLE CLASS WHO'LL GET IT RIGHT!

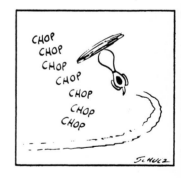

MA'AM?

HOW COME WE'VE ONLY BEEN STUDYING ABOUT MEN IN HISTORY?

AREN'T WE GOING TO STUDY ABOUT WOMEN?

I HAD A GRANDMOTHER WHO WAS KIND OF CUTE!

MY GRANDMOTHER HELPED TO MAKE THIS COUNTRY GREAT!

DURING WORLD WAR II, SHE WORKED AS A RIVETER, AND WROTE LETTERS TO SEVENTEEN SERVICEMEN!

TALK ABOUT WOMEN IN HISTORY...

LET'S HEAR IT FOR MY GRANDMOTHER!!

MY GRANDMOTHER LOVED TO DANCE

EVERY SATURDAY NIGHT SHE AND HER FRIENDS WENT TO THIS LITTLE PLACE THAT HAD A JUKE BOX, AND A DANCE FLOOR AND SIX BOOTHS...

SHE WAS THE FIRST ONE TO CARVE THOSE IMMORTAL WORDS ON THE BACK OF ONE OF THE BOOTHS, "KILROY WAS HERE"

ACTUALLY, ALTHOUGH GRANDMA WAS A LOT OF FUN, SHE WASN'T VERY CREATIVE!

AND SO, WORLD WAR II CAME TO AN END...

MY GRANDMOTHER LEFT HER JOB IN THE DEFENSE PLANT, AND WENT TO WORK FOR THE TELEPHONE COMPANY...

WE NEED TO STUDY THE LIVES OF GREAT WOMEN LIKE MY GRANDMOTHER... TALK TO YOUR OWN GRANDMOTHER TODAY... ASK HER QUESTIONS...

YOU'LL FIND SHE KNOWS MORE THAN PEANUT BUTTER COOKIES! THANK YOU!

I GOT AN "A" ON MY REPORT ABOUT MY GRANDMOTHER!

MY TEACHER SAID IT GAVE A UNIQUE PICTURE OF LIFE DURING WORLD WAR II

WAS YOUR GRANDFATHER IN WORLD WAR II?

NO, BUT HE'S SEEN "VICTORY AT SEA" TWELVE TIMES!

YES, MA'AM..

MY REPORT IS READY

ONE QUESTION...

DO YOU WISH ME TO VERBALIZE OR ORALIZE?

MY REPORT IS ON THE IMPORTANCE OF READING

IS KNOWING HOW TO READ IMPORTANT?

IT CERTAINLY IS

IT KEEPS YOU FROM BUMPING INTO THINGS!

IS READING IMPORTANT? YES!

IF YOU DIDN'T KNOW HOW TO READ, HOW COULD YOU READ "WAR AND PEACE"?

IF YOU DON'T READ "WAR AND PEACE," LEO TOLSTOY WILL HATE YOU!

DO YOU WANT TO BE HATED BY LEO TOLSTOY?

I REPEAT... READING IS IMPORTANT!

LET'S SAY, FOR INSTANCE, THAT YOU GET A LETTER FROM YOUR GRANDMOTHER..

YOU WANT TO BE ABLE TO READ WHAT SHE SAYS, DON'T YOU?

YOU THINK SHE'S WRITING JUST FOR HER HEALTH?

HERE'S SOMETHING ELSE TO THINK ABOUT..

DO YOU KNOW WHAT FRANCIS BACON SAID ABOUT READING?

"READING MAKETH A FULL MAN, CONFERENCE A READY MAN AND WRITING AN EXACT MAN"

THEN AGAIN WHAT DID SHE KNOW?

 SCHOOL STARTS NEXT WEEK

 I'M NOT READY TO GO BACK...

 WHAT WILL IT TAKE TO GET YOU READY TO GO BACK?

 BRIBERY!

 I CAN'T GO TO SCHOOL UNTIL I GET A NEW LUNCH BOX!

 WHAT'S WRONG WITH YOUR OLD LUNCH BOX?

 THE KID WHO SAT ACROSS THE AISLE FROM ME LAST YEAR PICKED IT UP...

 AFTER I THREW IT AT HIM, HE PICKED IT UP!

 SCHOOL STARTS TOMORROW.. ARE YOU READY?

 I'M READY! BY GOLLY, I'M MORE THAN READY!

 THIS IS MY YEAR FOR REVENGE

 I'D LIKE TO WRITE ON A VANDAL!

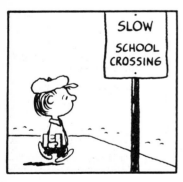 SLOW SCHOOL CROSSING

 JAMES STREET ELEMENTARY SCHOOL

 USE ONLY AS DIRECTED

 "MY SUMMER VACATION"

 THIS SUMMER I VISITED MY GRANDFATHER'S RANCH.. WELL, I GUESS IT ISN'T EXACTLY A RANCH...

 HE LIVES SORT OF IN THE COUNTRY...KIND OF ON THE EDGE OF TOWN...

 ACTUALLY, HE HAS AN APARTMENT OVER A DRUG STORE!

HEY, FRANKLIN, SHE STUCK A GOLD STAR ON YOUR PAPER!

THE TEACHER NEVER STICKS A STAR ON ANY OF MY PAPERS...

I COULDN'T GET A STAR ON A CHRISTMAS TREE!

SORRY, MA'AM!

I'VE NEVER GOTTEN A GOLD STAR FOR ANYTHING, MARCIE

THE TEACHER GIVES GOLD STARS FOR SPELLING, FOR ATTENDANCE, FOR DRINKING MILK AND FOR EVERYTHING, BUT I NEVER GET A GOLD STAR!

HAVE YOU EVER GOTTEN A GOLD STAR, MARCIE?

I GOT ONE FOR SPELLING, ONE FOR ATTENDANCE, ONE FOR DRINKING MILK, ONE FOR..

FORGET IT, MARCIE!

MA'AM, MAY I SEE YOUR BOX OF LITTLE GOLD STARS?

WOW! LOOK AT 'EM ALL! LOOK HOW SHINY THEY ARE!

THE NEXT TIME YOU STICK SOME ON ANY PAPERS, MA'AM, LET ME KNOW...

I'LL LICK 'EM FOR YOU!

YOUR BOX OF GOLD STARS? NO, MA'AM, I DON'T HAVE IT

I PUT IT BACK ON YOUR DESK, REMEMBER? I WOULDN'T TAKE YOUR BOX OF GOLD STARS, MA'AM...

I'M AN HONEST PERSON...I EVEN HAVE AN HONEST FACE..

IT'S A LITTLE DISORGANIZED, BUT IT'S HONEST!

GUESS WHAT, CHUCK! MISS TENURE ACCUSED ME OF STEALING HER BOX OF GOLD STARS...

THAT'S HARD TO BELIEVE..

YOU'RE NOT KIDDING, CHUCK! IS MY STUPID ATTORNEY AROUND THERE ANY PLACE?

YES, HE'S RIGHT HERE...

"CURSE ON ALL LAWS BUT THOSE WHICH LOVE HAS MADE!"

WHY WOULD I TAKE A BOX OF GOLD STARS, CHUCK?

MAYBE MISS TENURE WASN'T ACCUSING YOU... MAYBE SHE WAS JUST ASKING...

I DON'T KNOW... I THINK I'M JUST GONNA NEED A GOOD ATTORNEY

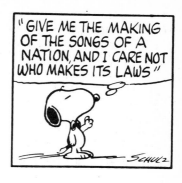

"GIVE ME THE MAKING OF THE SONGS OF A NATION, AND I CARE NOT WHO MAKES ITS LAWS"

I DIDN'T STEAL THAT BOX OF GOLD STARS, SNOOPY, BUT I'M GOING TO FIND OUT WHO DID...

NOW, HERE'S MY SECRET PLAN...

I LOVE SECRET PLANS

YOU'LL WEAR THIS WIG, SEE, AND YOU'LL SIT IN MY SEAT AT SCHOOL

WHILE YOU'RE DOING THAT, I'LL SNEAK AROUND, AND FIND OUT WHO TOOK THE GOLD STARS!

YOU LOOK SMALLER TODAY, SIR, AND YOU SEEM QUIETER....

AREN'T YOU FEELING WELL, SIR?

! ?

WHAT KIND OF ILLNESS MAKES YOUR BODY SHRINK BUT YOUR NOSE GET BIGGER?

PSST!

?

THIS IS A HARD TEST, ISN'T IT, SIR?

WHAT DID YOU PUT DOWN FOR THE LAST QUESTION?

SIR, WHAT ARE YOU DOING OUT HERE IN THE HALLWAY?

QUIET, MARCIE

I'M IN DISGUISE! I'M TRYING TO FIND OUT WHO TOOK THE BOX OF GOLD STARS...

BUT I JUST SAW YOU SITTING AT YOUR DESK...

THAT'S MY ATTORNEY... HE'S ALSO IN DISGUISE...

"I BEFORE E EXCEPT AFTER C"

YES, MA'AM..I'M HANS HANSEN, THE NEW CUSTODIAN...

JUST GO ON WITH YOUR TEACHING, MA'AM..I'LL SWEEP UP A BIT AND EMPTY THE WASTEBASKETS...

OH, I'M DREAMING OF MY SWEETHEART IN MINNEAPOLIS AND MY MOTHER IN ST.PAUL!

SORRY, MA'AM..I CAN'T HELP SINGING WHILE I SWEEP...

LOOK WHAT I FOUND IN YOUR WASTEBASKET, MISS TENURE... YOUR BOX OF GOLD STARS!

I'LL BET YOU THOUGHT ONE OF YOUR PUPILS STOLE IT, DIDN'T YOU?

THEY WOULDN'T DO ANYTHING LIKE THAT... ESPECIALLY THAT CUTE ONE WITH THE BEAUTIFUL HAIR AND THE FRECKLES..

AND I FOUND THE BOX OF GOLD STARS IN MISS TENURE'S WASTEBASKET

I'M GLAD EVERYTHING TURNED OUT ALL RIGHT FOR YOU, SIR...

SNOOPY DID WELL SITTING AT YOUR DESK, TOO..

HE GOT A STAR ON HIS TEST!

AAUGH!

I CAN'T GO TO SCHOOL TODAY... MY RIGHT SHOULDER HURTS...

IF I SHOULD HAPPEN TO KNOW AN ANSWER, I WOULDN'T BE ABLE TO RAISE MY HAND

C'MON, GET UP! YOU CAN ALWAYS RAISE YOUR OTHER HAND..

YOU EXPECT ME TO ANSWER QUESTIONS LEFT-HANDED?!

JUST BEFORE THE TEST BEGAN, OUR TEACHER GOES, "DOES EVERYONE HAVE A PENCIL?"

THIS FAT KID ACROSS THE AISLE FROM ME GOES, "I DON'T!"

THEN THIS OTHER KID WITH THE GLASSES GOES, "SURE YOU DO... YOU HAVE MINE!"

WHATEVER HAPPENED TO THE WORD "SAID"?

IF WE EVER HAVE AN INK SHORTAGE, YOU'RE GONNA BE BLAMED!

THIS IS MY REPORT ON EMERALDS..CLEOPATRA OWNED LOTS OF EMERALDS BECAUSE SHE HAD HER OWN EMERALD MINE...

EMERALDS, UNLIKE OTHER STONES, APPEAR THE SAME COLOR IN ARTIFICIAL LIGHT AS IN SUNLIGHT...

AND THAT'S ALL I KNOW ABOUT EMERALDS

WHAT I COULD TELL YOU ABOUT CLEOPATRA, HOWEVER, WOULD MAKE YOUR HEAD SPIN!

YESTERDAY WE TALKED ABOUT EMERALDS...

TODAY MY REPORT IS ON THE MOONSTONE... THIS IS A MYSTERIOUS GEM SURROUNDED BY MANY INTRIGUING LEGENDS...

IT HAS BEEN SAID THAT THE MOONSTONE CAN BANISH FEARS

FRANKLY, HOWEVER, I WOULDN'T COUNT ON IT IF YOU'RE ABOUT TO GET MUGGED

MOONSTONES COME FROM CEYLON

THEY ARE CUT IN THE SHAPE OF A DOME TO ACCENT THE PLAY OF LIGHT

THEY SAY THIS MAKES THE MOONSTONE LOOK LIKE A RAINDROP SEEN THROUGH THE MIST AT EARLY DAWN

I WOULDN'T KNOW BECAUSE I NEVER GET UP THAT EARLY...

THIS CONCLUDES MY REPORT ON GEMS AND JEWELRY... ARE THERE ANY QUESTIONS?

YES, YOU IN THE BACK ROW...YOUR QUESTION, PLEASE

NO, YOU SHOULD NOT WEAR YOUR JEWELRY IF YOU ARE GOING TO SLIDE INTO SECOND BASE

SEEING THE STUPID TREND THAT THESE QUESTIONS ARE ABOUT TO TAKE, I WILL NOW SIT DOWN!

THIS IS MY BOOK REPORT

I WAS GOING TO SAY THAT THIS WAS, QUITE SIMPLY, THE BEST BOOK I HAVE EVER READ...

HOWEVER, I'VE CHANGED MY MIND

I HATE PEOPLE WHO SAY, "QUITE SIMPLY"

WILL YOU WALK HOME FROM SCHOOL WITH ME, LINUS?

I THINK THE POWERS OF DARKNESS ARE OUT TO GET ME...

I DOUBT IF I COULD EVER PROTECT YOU FROM THE POWERS OF DARKNESS

HOW ABOUT A THIRD-GRADER WHO CLAIMS I BROKE HIS RULER?

IT'S FOR YOU...SOME KID FROM SCHOOL...

HE SAYS YOU BORROWED HIS RULER, AND THEN YOU BROKE IT...IS THAT TRUE?

IT WASN'T MY FAULT

I WAS MEASURING THE STREET, AND A TRUCK RAN OVER IT!

NOW IF SOME KID COMES UP, AND STARTS ASKING ABOUT A RULER, YOU HOLD HIM OFF...

HOLD HIM OFF?

YES, YOU HOLD HIM OFF WHILE I RUN FOR IT!

WHAT IF HE TRIES TO HIT ME?

REASON WITH HIM

TELL HIM HIS STUPID RULER WOULDN'T HAVE BEEN ANY GOOD AFTER WE SWITCHED TO METRICS, ANYWAY!

IT WAS A TWELVE INCH RULER? I SEE...

IT'S THAT KID FROM SCHOOL AGAIN...HE WANTS HIS RULER...

SHALL I TELL HIM A TRUCK RAN OVER IT?

ASK HIM IF HE'LL SETTLE FOR THREE FOUR-INCH ONES

PROBLEM NUMBER SIX...

"HOW MANY GALLONS OF CREAM CONTAINING 25% BUTTER FAT AND MILK CONTAINING 3½% BUTTER FAT MUST BE MIXED TO..

..OBTAIN 50 GALLONS OF CREAM CONTAINING 12½% BUTTER FAT?"

MA'AM, WOULD YOU SETTLE FOR TWENTY PUSH-UPS?

MY NAME IS EUDORA, AND I'M NEW IN THIS CLASS

OUR FAMILY JUST MOVED HERE FROM OUT OF STATE

NO, MA'AM...I DON'T KNOW WHICH STATE

I DON'T EVEN KNOW WHERE I AM NOW!

WHAT ARE YOU EATING FOR LUNCH, EUDORA?

THIS IS A CHOCOLATE SANDWICH

I PUT A CHOCOLATE BAR BETWEEN TWO SLICES OF DARK BREAD

I OFTEN WONDER HOW IT WOULD TASTE WITH GRAVY ON IT...

THIS IS MY LITERATURE REPORT

THE BOOK I CHOSE TO READ WAS THE TV GUIDE

MA'AM?

I WAS AFRAID OF THAT!

EUDORA! WHAT ARE YOU DOING HERE? THERE'S NO SCHOOL ON SATURDAY!

THERE ISN'T? THAT EXPLAINS EVERYTHING...

SATURDAY'S THE ONLY DAY I NEVER GET ANYTHING WRONG

I WONDER IF IT'S TOO LATE TO BECOME A DISCO...

"THIS IS MY CHRISTMAS STORY..." SANTA AND HIS RAIN GEAR"

"WHEN SANTA LEFT THE NORTH POLE THAT EVENING, A GENTLE MIST WAS FALLING"

"IN HIS YELLOW SLICKER AND BIG RUBBER BOOTS, HE SET OUT ON HIS ANNUAL JOURNEY"

"IT WAS CHRISTMAS EVE, AND SOON CHILDREN AROUND THE WORLD WOULD BE HEARING THE SOUND OF SANTA AND HIS RAIN GEAR"

"LITTLE GEORGE WAS WAITING FOR SANTA TO COME"

"SUDDENLY HE HEARD THE SOUND OF SOMEONE WALKING ON THE ROOF! IT WAS A MAN IN A YELLOW SLICKER AND BIG RUBBER BOOTS!"

"'I SAW HIM!' SHOUTED LITTLE GEORGE..'I SAW SANTA AND HIS RAIN GEAR'"

DON'T SQUIRM, MA'AM, THERE'S MORE TO COME!

"THE RAIN CAME DOWN HARDER AND HARDER"

"BUT THE MAN IN THE YELLOW SLICKER AND BIG RUBBER BOOTS NEVER FALTERED"

"ANOTHER CHRISTMAS EVE HAD PASSED, AND SANTA AND HIS RAIN GEAR HAD DONE THEIR JOB! THE END"

HA HA HA! HA HA HA! HA HA!

A FINE BROTHER YOU ARE! YOU LET ME MAKE A FOOL OUT OF MYSELF!!

IT ISN'T RAIN GEAR! IT'S REINDEER! WHY DIDN'T YOU TELL ME?!

THEY ALL LAUGHED AT ME! EVEN THE TEACHER LAUGHED AT ME! I'LL NEVER BE ABLE TO GO TO THAT SCHOOL AGAIN!

POOR SWEET BABY...

SNIF!

THEY SURE HAD THEIR NERVE LAUGHING AT MY STORY.... HA!

HOW ABOUT THIS THING WITH ALL THE REINDEER PULLING THE SLEIGH THROUGH THE AIR? NO WAY!

I DON'T CARE HOW MANY REINDEER HE HAD, THEY COULD NEVER PRODUCE ENOUGH LIFT TO GET A SLED IN THE AIR...

NO WAY, HUH, BIG BROTHER?

NO WAY! MERRY CHRISTMAS!

YES, MA'AM? YOU WANT ME TO WORK OUT THE PROBLEM AT THE BOARD?

WELL, LET'S SEE.. WE HAVE THESE NUMBERS HERE, DON'T WE?

THESE ARE NICE NUMBERS, MA'AM..

A FOUR, A SIX, A SEVEN, AN EIGHT, A FIVE AND A TWO

OH, YES, AND WE ALSO HAVE AN X ...

WELL, THE PROBLEM SEEMS TO BE TO TRY TO FIND OUT WHAT THIS X IS DOING AMONG ALL THESE NUMBERS...

IS HE AN OUT-SIDER? WAS HE INVITED TO JOIN THE GROUP? IT'S AN INTERESTING QUESTION...

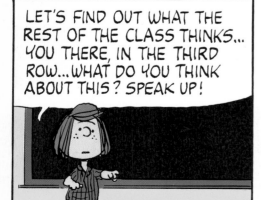
LET'S FIND OUT WHAT THE REST OF THE CLASS THINKS... YOU THERE, IN THE THIRD ROW...WHAT DO YOU THINK ABOUT THIS? SPEAK UP!

MA'AM?

RATS! THREE MORE MINUTES AND THE BELL WOULD HAVE RUNG!

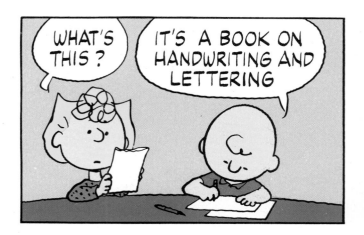

WHAT'S THIS?

IT'S A BOOK ON HANDWRITING AND LETTERING

"AFTER PRACTICING THE CORRECT HAND MOVEMENTS WITH A PENCIL, YOU ARE NOW READY FOR PEN AND INK"

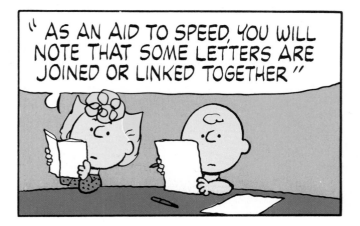

"AS AN AID TO SPEED, YOU WILL NOTE THAT SOME LETTERS ARE JOINED OR LINKED TOGETHER"

"DURING PRACTICE, HOWEVER, IT IS BEST NOT TO TRY TO LINK UP CERTAIN LETTERS..."

I THINK YOU LINKED THEM UP!

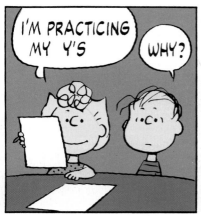

YOU KNOW WHAT I AM, MARCIE? I'M A WEED!

THE WORLD IS FILLED WITH BEAUTIFUL PLANTS AND FLOWERS, BUT I'M JUST AN UGLY WEED

I'M A POOR UGLY WEED TRYING TO PUSH HER WAY UP THROUGH THE SIDEWALK OF LIFE!

THAT'S A GREAT METAPHOR, SIR

DID YOU KNOW THAT WEEDS HAVE A WIDE TOLERANCE FOR ENVIRONMENTAL CONDITIONS AND THE RARE ABILITY TO EXPLOIT RECENTLY DISTURBED TERRAIN?

WHAT IN THE WORLD DOES THAT MEAN?

YOU CAN ROLL WITH THE PUNCHES, SIR!

BY GOLLY, MARCIE, I THINK YOU'RE RIGHT...

I'VE GOT MY CONFIDENCE BACK, MA'AM! ASK ME ANYTHING! GIVE ME YOUR BEST SHOT!!

I'LL BET THE PRINCIPAL WOULD BE SURPRISED TO FIND A WEED GROWING IN FRONT OF HIS OFFICE...

GETTING READY FOR BED CAN BE A REAL CHORE...

YOU SHOULD MAKE SURE YOUR BOOKS AND THINGS ARE SET PROPERLY FOR SCHOOL THE NEXT DAY...

THEN YOU HAVE TO GET YOUR GLASS OF MILK, AND SAY, "GOOD NIGHT" TO YOUR DOG...

AND THEN YOU HAVE TO BE ABSOLUTELY SURE THAT YOU'VE TAKEN ALL THE...

AAUGH!

...PINS OUT OF YOUR NEW PAJAMAS!

 YOU KNOW WHAT I THINK YOU HAVE, SIR? YOU HAVE "MATH ANXIETY"

 IF I ASKED YOU HOW MANY WAYS THAT NINE BOOKS COULD BE ARRANGED ON A SHELF, WHAT WOULD BE YOUR FIRST REACTION?

 AAUGHH!

 SEE? YOU HAVE "MATH ANXIETY"

 "HOW MANY ANGELS CAN STAND ON THE HEAD OF A PIN?"

 THIS MUST BE KIND OF A PHILOSOPHICAL QUESTION, HUH, MA'AM?

 THE HEAD OF A PIN, HUH? BOY, THAT'S A HARD ONE...

 HOW ABOUT A PAPER CLIP?

 GET THIS, CHUCK... SHE ASKS US HOW MANY ANGELS CAN STAND ON THE HEAD OF A PIN!

 WHAT KIND OF A QUESTION IS THAT, CHUCK? HOW CAN YOU ANSWER SOMETHING LIKE THAT?

 YOU CAN'T, PATTY... IT'S AN OLD THEOLOGICAL PROBLEM... THERE REALLY IS NO ANSWER...

 THAT'S TOO BAD... I PUT DOWN, "EIGHT, IF THEY'RE SKINNY, AND FOUR IF THEY'RE FAT!"

 YOU CAN'T SAY HOW MANY ANGELS CAN STAND ON THE HEAD OF A PIN, SIR... THERE IS NO ANSWER!

 WELL, THAT'S JUST GREAT, MARCIE! IF I TRY TO ANSWER A QUESTION, I'M WRONG!

 IF I DON'T ANSWER A QUESTION, I'M RIGHT!

 THAT'S EDUCATION, SIR!

 *At first the cowboy rode his horse very fast.*

 *Soon, however, he had to slow down.*

 *The countryside was becoming too*

 *hillllllllly.*

"YIPE YIPE YIPE," WENT THE DOG

"YIPE YIPE YIPE YIPE YIPE YIPE YIPE YIPE YIPE YIPE YIPE YIPE YIPE YIPE YIPE YIPE..."

MA'AM?

OKAY, BUT IT'S SURE GONNA SPOIL THE EFFECT!

SORRY ABOUT MY MATH PAPER, MA'AM

ON MY WAY TO SCHOOL THIS MORNING, I SORT OF DROPPED IT IN THE MUD

MAYBE YOU CAN KIND OF BRUSH IT OFF A BIT WITH YOUR SLEEVE.. WANNA TRY IT?

I GUESS NOT

SPELLING BEE?

NO, MA'AM..NOT UNLESS YOU SAY I HAVE TO

GO AHEAD, FRANKLIN... YOU CAN DO IT...

MAYBE I COULD JUST BE IN THE PRO-AM...

INSCRUTABLE?

NO, MA'AM... I CAN'T SPELL INSCRUTABLE

YOU SAID, IF I TOOK PART IN THE SPELLING BEE, ALL I'D HAVE TO DO IS SPELL WORDS...

YOU DIDN'T SAY I HAD TO SPELL 'EM RIGHT!

I WAS RUNNER-UP IN THE SPELLING BEE! HOW ABOUT THAT?

YOU WEREN'T RUNNER-UP, FRANKLIN...

YOU CAME IN SIXTEENTH...

I WAS RUNNER-UP TO THE KID WHO CAME IN FIFTEENTH!

IF YOU DON'T HELP ME WORK FOR WOMEN IN SPORTS, MARCIE, I'LL NEVER INTRODUCE YOU TO BILLIE JEAN KING!

YOU DON'T EVEN KNOW BILLIE JEAN KING, SIR

HOW CAN YOU SAY "BILLIE JEAN KING, MAY I PRESENT MARCIE?" WHEN YOU DON'T KNOW BILLIE JEAN KING?

ASK HER A HARD QUESTION, MA'AM! SHE'S DRIVING ME CRAZY!

Z

Z

SORRY, MA'AM..I CAN'T RAISE MY HEAD...

MAYBE IF YOU WALKED AROUND TO THE SIDE OF THE ROOM AND STOOD THERE JUST A LITTLE TO THE LEFT OF THE RADIATOR..

TRUE? WHO KNOWS? FALSE? ONLY TIME WILL TELL...

PERHAPS... COULD BE... MAYBE..I DOUBT IT... DON'T COUNT ON IT...

MAYBE IN THE LONG RUN...IT ALL DEPENDS... WEATHER PERMITTING

SOME OF US, MA'AM, SEE EVERYTHING IN SHADES OF GRAY

HOW DID YOU DO ON THE TEST, SIR?

I GOT TWO RIGHT OUT OF TWENTY

THAT WASN'T VERY GOOD, SIR...

FROM ALL I'VE HEARD, MARCIE, IT'S LONELY AT THE TOP!

WHY DO WE HAVE TO GO ON FIELD TRIPS?

SO THE CUSTODIANS CAN SWEEP OUR ROOM

WHAT IF WE GET MUGGED?

DON'T WORRY..

MY SWEET BABBOO WILL TAKE CARE OF US

I'M NOT YOUR SWEET BABBOO!

HE REALLY IS..HE'S JUST TOO SHY TO ADMIT IT

ANYONE IN THE BACK WANNA CHANGE SEATS?

MA'AM, I THINK THE CEILING IS LEAKING...

YES, MA'AM, RIGHT UP THERE...SEE?

I TOLD HER ABOUT IT, SIR

THANKS, MARCIE.. I DON'T LIKE TO BE THE KIND WHO COMPLAINS

YES, MA'AM, I GUESS THAT WORKS...

THANK YOU FOR TELLING THE CUSTODIAN ABOUT THE LEAK IN THE CEILING, MA'AM...

HE CERTAINLY TOOK CARE OF IT FAST, DIDN'T HE, SIR?

YOU MIGHT SAY THAT..

GUESS WHAT, SIR..

I HEARD THAT THE BOARD OF EDUCATION AND THE PRINCIPAL HAVE BEEN ARGUING ABOUT THE LEAK IN THE CEILING...

THEY CAN'T DECIDE WHAT TO DO...I IMAGINE IT'S A FINANCIAL PROBLEM, WOULDN'T YOU SAY, SIR?

JUST EMPTY THE PAN AGAIN WILL YOU, MARCIE?

THE PRINCIPAL TOLD THE TEACHER SHE MIGHT CONSIDER MOVING YOU TO ANOTHER DESK, SIR

BUT SHE SAID SHE CAN'T DO THAT

WHY NOT?

SHE SAID IT WOULD DESTROY HER ALPHABETICAL SEATING ARRANGEMENT

I THINK IT'S STOPPED RAINING, SIR

YOU CAN TAKE THE PAN OFF YOUR HEAD NOW

MAYBE YOU COULD GIVE OUR CLASS A REPORT ON THE ANNUAL RAINFALL IN THIS AREA...

READ THIS, MARCIE..IT'S ALL ABOUT A SCHOOL FOR GIFTED CHILDREN

I'VE NEVER HEARD OF A SCHOOL BEFORE THAT GIVES YOU THINGS

I DON'T THINK IT MEANS THAT, SIR

I'D SETTLE FOR JUST A T-SHIRT

"ACE SCHOOL FOR GIFTED CHILDREN"..HOW ABOUT THAT, CHUCK?

JUST THINK..A SCHOOL THAT GIVES YOU PRESENTS! I'M GONNA APPLY!

ARE YOU SURE YOU'RE READING THAT RIGHT?

THE FIRST THINGS I'M GONNA ASK FOR ARE SOME NEW SKATES AND MAYBE A DART BOARD...

I'M GOING OVER TO THE SCHOOL FOR GIFTED CHILDREN, MARCIE...I DON'T SUPPOSE YOU WANT TO COME ALONG..

I DON'T THINK SO, SIR

I IMAGINE IT'S A LOT LIKE PLAYING IN A PRO-AM

FIRST YOU CHECK IN, AND THEN YOU PICK UP YOUR GIFTS

I DON'T THINK IT'S LIKE THAT AT ALL, SIR...

I JUST WISH I HAD KNOWN ABOUT THIS WAY BACK IN KINDERGARTEN..

GOOD AFTERNOON, MA'AM.. IS THIS THE SCHOOL FOR GIFTED CHILDREN?

I'D LIKE TO ENROLL

THIS BAG? OH, THIS IS FOR THE GIFTS

IF IT ISN'T BIG ENOUGH, I CAN BRING ANOTHER ONE TOMORROW

SHE WENT OVER TO A SCHOOL FOR GIFTED CHILDREN, CHARLES..SHE THINKS THEY'RE GOING TO GIVE HER THINGS...

I DON'T KNOW WHAT TO DO ABOUT HER, CHARLES.. SHE NEVER LISTENS...

CHARLES? ARE YOU THERE? WHO AM I TALKING TO?

IF I BARK, IT'LL SCARE HER TO DEATH...

YES, MA'AM..IF THIS IS THE SCHOOL FOR GIFTED CHILDREN, I'D LIKE TO ENROLL...

DO I THINK I'M GIFTED?

I'M NOT SURE

I USUALLY GET A FEW THINGS FOR MY BIRTHDAY AND FOR CHRISTMAS, BUT THAT'S ABOUT IT...

YES, MA'AM, I READ IN THE PAPER ABOUT YOUR SCHOOL FOR GIFTED CHILDREN

MY SCHOOL IS ALL RIGHT, BUT I LIKE YOUR APPROACH BETTER

IS THIS BAG GOING TO BE BIG ENOUGH FOR ALL THE GIFTS?

THESE ARE MY CLOTHING AND SHOE SIZES..IF YOU GIVE OUT ICE SKATES, I'D LIKE THEM ABOUT ONE SIZE SMALLER...

MISUNDERSTANDING? ISN'T THIS THE SCHOOL FOR GIFTED CHILDREN? AREN'T YOU GONNA FILL MY BAG WITH GIFTS?

BUT I THOUGHT... I WAS SURE THAT... AREN'T YOU... I MEAN... I...

OH, NO!

IF ANYONE ASKS FOR ME, I WAS NEVER HERE!

MARCIE, YOU LET ME GO TO THAT SCHOOL, AND MAKE A FOOL OF MYSELF!

YOU WOULDN'T LISTEN TO ME, SIR

YOU DIDN'T TRY HARD ENOUGH

YOU COULD HAVE STOPPED ME IF YOU HAD REALLY TRIED

IF I HAD TRIED TO STOP YOU, YOU WOULD HAVE HIT ME...

YOU COULD HAVE DUCKED

SHE'S GONE, CHARLES! PEPPERMINT PATTY HAS LEFT TOWN!

BUT I JUST TALKED TO HER YESTERDAY...

I THINK SHE WAS MORE DEPRESSED THAN WE THOUGHT, CHARLES... WHERE DO YOU THINK SHE WENT?

"SPIKE'S REAL ESTATE..NEEDLES, CALIFORNIA"...WELL, I'M NOT REALLY READY TO BUY... COULDN'T YOU JUST FIND ME A PLACE TO STAY?

I NEED TO TALK TO SOMEONE WHO KNOWS WHAT IT'S LIKE TO FEEL LIKE A FOOL

SOMEONE WHO KNOWS WHAT IT'S LIKE TO BE HUMILIATED...

SOMEONE WHO'S BEEN DISGRACED, BEATEN AND DEGRADED.... SOMEONE WHO'S BEEN THERE...

WHAT DO YOU HAVE THERE, SIR?

IT'S A BOOK ON FIRST AID, MARCIE

HERE'S THE CHAPTER I WAS LOOKING FOR...

"WHAT TO DO IN CASE OF STUPIDITY"

I KNOW, MA'AM! I KNOW!

THE ANSWER IS, "THE WHOLE WORLD"

IT ISN'T? SORRY, MA'AM

I THOUGHT FOR SURE THE ANSWER WOULD BE IN THERE SOME PLACE

I HAVE IT ALL FIGURED OUT, MARCIE...

THE WAY I SEE IT, THERE SEEM TO BE MORE QUESTIONS THAN THERE ARE ANSWERS

SO?

SO TRY TO BE THE ONE WHO ASKS THE QUESTIONS!

THIS IS MY REPORT ON THE PAST

THE PAST HAS ALWAYS INTERESTED PEOPLE

I MUST ADMIT, HOWEVER, THAT I DON'T KNOW MUCH ABOUT IT

I WASN'T HERE WHEN IT HAPPENED

ME?

YES, MA'AM... I AGREE..

THE ANSWER REALLY LIES DEEP WITHIN THE HEARTS OF ALL OF US

THE ANSWER IS ACTUALLY A PART OF OUR HERITAGE, OUR CULTURE, OUR WHOLE WAY OF LIVING...

THE ANSWER IS THE WAY EACH OF US CONTRIBUTES A LITTLE SOMETHING TO OUR FUTURE!

THAT WAS VERY GOOD, SIR

THANK YOU, MARCIE

EXCEPT THE ANSWER WAS "TWELVE"!

SEVEN, EIGHT, NINE, TEN! HA!!

"7+3=10"...THAT'S AN EASY ONE, MARCIE...

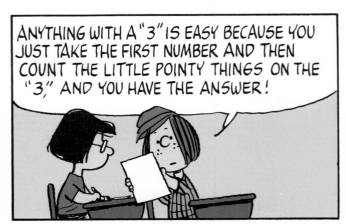

ANYTHING WITH A "3" IS EASY BECAUSE YOU JUST TAKE THE FIRST NUMBER AND THEN COUNT THE LITTLE POINTY THINGS ON THE "3," AND YOU HAVE THE ANSWER!

WHAT ABOUT "TWELVES," SIR?

NO ONE CAN BE EXPECTED TO ANSWER A PROBLEM WITH A "TWELVE" IN IT!

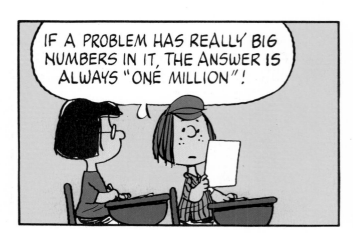

IF A PROBLEM HAS REALLY BIG NUMBERS IN IT, THE ANSWER IS ALWAYS "ONE MILLION"!

MATH IS LIKE LEARNING A FOREIGN LANGUAGE, MARCIE...NO MATTER WHAT YOU SAY, IT'S GOING TO BE WRONG ANYWAY!

LET'S SEE..."NINE PLUS THREE"...I TAKE THE NINE AND COUNT THE LITTLE POINTY THINGS ON THE THREE...TEN, ELEVEN, TWELVE...THE ANSWER IS "TWELVE"... HA!!

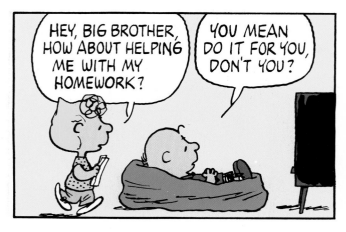

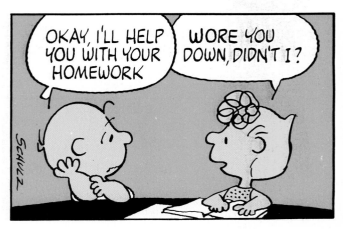

WOW!

LOOK, MARCIE, LOOK!

I GOT AN "A" ON MY FINAL REPORT CARD!

I'VE NEVER GOTTEN AN "A" BEFORE! HOW ABOUT THAT?

ALL I SEE ARE A BUNCH OF "D MINUSES," SIR

LOOK AT THE TOP, MARCIE.. IT'S RIGHT THERE AT THE TOP...

IT SAYS, "REPORT CARD," SIR..THIS "A" IS JUST PART OF THE WORD...

RATS! NOT GETTING AN "A" WHEN YOU THINK YOU DID IS LIKE LOSING A TIE BREAKER..

YES, MA'AM?

WHAT WAS THE NAME OF THE KING WHOSE DAUGHTER'S MARRIAGE MADE POSSIBLE THE UNIFICATION OF DENMARK AND NORWAY IN 1380?

WOW! THAT'S THE KIND OF QUESTION THAT MAKES YOUR TEMPLES THROB..

IT MAKES YOUR EARS RING AND YOUR HAIR STAND ON END...

IT MAKES YOUR EYES WATER, YOUR CHEEKS BURN, YOUR MOUTH TURN DRY AND YOUR TEETH ACHE...

A QUESTION LIKE THAT CAN DESTROY YOUR WHOLE HEAD!

I'M PRACTICING MY SWIRLS

THEY LOOK MORE LIKE OVALS TO ME..

DON'T BE RIDICULOUS! OVALS ARE MORE OVALLY! CAN'T YOU TELL A SWIRL FROM AN OVAL?

LOOK HOW SWIRLY THESE ARE!! THEY'RE NOT OVALLY AT ALL!

IF I WANTED TO MAKE OVALS, I'D MAKE OVALS! WHAT'S WRONG WITH YOU, ANYWAY?

ANYONE WHO CAN'T TELL A SWIRL FROM AN OVAL NEEDS GLASSES!

AND WHO ASKED YOU?

YES, MA'AM.. MORE THAN READY...

THEY'RE GONNA LOVE THIS, MARCIE!

THIS IS MY REPORT ON "WHAT I DID THIS SUMMER"... AT THE CONCLUSION, I WILL ANSWER QUESTIONS..

ONE DAY LATE IN THE SUMMER, I WAS LYING IN A MEADOW, WHEN SUDDENLY, A BUTTERFLY LANDED ON MY NOSE!

WELL, I DIDN'T WANT TO BRUSH IT AWAY BECAUSE I MIGHT HURT IT...

AFTER A WHILE I MUST HAVE DOZED OFF.. WHEN I OPENED MY EYES, THE BUTTERFLY WAS GONE!

YOU'LL NEVER GUESS WHAT HAPPENED... IT HAD TURNED INTO AN ANGEL, AND FLOWN AWAY!

WELL, THIS WAS OBVIOUSLY A MIRACLE! I HAD BEEN CHOSEN TO BRING A MESSAGE TO THE WORLD!

WHAT WAS THIS MESSAGE I WAS TO BRING TO THE WORLD? AFTER MUCH THOUGHT, I DECIDED IT WAS THIS, "A FOUL BALL HIT BEHIND THIRD BASE IS THE SHORTSTOP'S PLAY!"

MA'AM, IF IT'S OKAY WITH YOU, I'LL TAKE THE QUESTIONS AFTER SCHOOL OUT IN THE ALLEY BEHIND THE GYM!

YOU LOOK LIKE YOU'RE SINKING, SIR...

I AM, MARCIE

I'M DROWNING IN A SEA OF UNANSWERED QUESTIONS...

NOW, I SUDDENLY SURFACE! I SPLASH FRANTICALLY... "HELP!" I CRY..."SAVE ME!"

NOW, I SINK FOR THE SECOND TIME...QUESTIONS POUR OVER MY HEAD..."WHO WAS VOLTAIRE?" "WHO WAS CATO THE ELDER?"

NOW, I COME UP FOR THE LAST TIME... SPUTTERING HALF-ANSWERS..SPITTING OUT VERBS, INFINITIVES, COMMAS...

I SINK BENEATH THE SURFACE.. I'M GONE, MARCIE... I'M GONE...

MARK THE SPOT WHERE YOU LAST SAW ME..MARK THE SPOT WHERE I DROWNED IN A SEA OF "D MINUSES" AND "INCOMPLETES"

ANOTHER SCHOLAR CAUGHT IN THE UNDERTOW, MA'AM